MW00807732

This book belongs to:

_____

My Parents Still Love Me

Even Though

They're Getting Divorced

A healing story and workbook
for children

Lois V. Nightingale, Ph.D.

Published by:
Nightingale Rose Publications
16960 East Bastanchury Road, Suite J
Yorba Linda, California 92886

Acknowledgements:

I want to thank the courageous parents who have shared their struggles and concerns about their children with me at my lectures and in therapy sessions. I am grateful to them for insights into parenting during divorce and am in awe of the self-confident and emotionally-centered children they are now raising.

I also want to express my gratitude to all those who encouraged me and gave me feedback throughout the process of creating this book. I want to thank Dave for his continuous support in editing and his belief in my projects. I want to thank Baz and Bambi for their attention to details and their flexibility with my crazy schedule so this book could happen. Kudos to dear Anna who has cultivated her artistic roots to surpass all previous horizons.

I want to thank those closest to me: Mike, Harry, Teddi, Barbara, and Karen, for their unwavering love and positive support.

And I wish to extend a special acknowledgment to all the non-custodial parents who sacrifice daily to meet the financial and emotional commitments to the children they love, in spite of possible animosity toward the other parent. Never doubt that your gifts to your children have a great impact on their future and the future of our world — and will be returned to you many times over.

Copyright © 2016, By Nightingale Rose Publications and Lois V. Nightingale PhD
Library of Congress: TXu 1-984-289
ISBN-13:-978-1-889755-01-4

All rights reserved. No part of this book may be reproduced or transmitted in any form or by any means, electronic or mechanical, including photocopying, recording, or by any information storage means, or retrieval system, without permission in writing from the publisher.

Published by Nightingale Rose Publications,
16960 E. Bastanchury Road, Suite J, Yorba Linda, California, 92886.

Artwork by Anna Fimmel and Blanca Apodaca
Book Design by Baz Here and Lois Nightingale
Author Photo by Baz Here

Summary: A fantasy story and workbook to educate, support
and help children and their families going through divorce.

Disclaimer:
This book is designed to provide information concerning the subject matter covered. It is not designed to take the place of professional counseling. If an adult or a child is having a particularly difficult time handling changes they are facing, it is important to seek professional help. If a child or an adult is experiencing signs of depression, severe anxiety reactions, or other severe psychological disturbances, it is important that they receive professional psychological help. Licensed therapists in your area can be found through the internet. Local psychiatric hospitals also give free referrals to persons requesting psychological assistance.

This book is dedicated
to parents who are struggling
with the complex challenges of helping
the children they love through a divorce.

CONTENTS

An Important Note to Parents, Counselors and Therapists
Useful suggestions for reading and using this book:

Parents
It is suggested that the child's parent(s), or other supportive adult, read this book before sharing it with the child. Concepts presented in the story may require adult support and further explanation. For a child to have greatest benefit from the story and activities, it is recommended that an adult read to, or along with, the child.

When dealing with strong emotions, children may have a shorter attention span than while watching TV or playing a video game. It is important not to rush kids through the story or the workbook pages. Children may prefer to hear the story and do the activities in sections, rather than all in one sitting. Many parents prefer to read through the entire story once (usually in parts, over 2 or 3 days) and then have children fill in the workbook pages upon a second reading. This allows a child to first understand that other children have gone through a similar experience and have come out all right. Children may feel freer to express their ideas and feelings if they know everything will turn out all right in the end.

It is also important to let the child know there are no "right" or "wrong" answers, and that there will be no judgments or criticisms made about their responses. Parents can let a child know they are free to do as many or as few of the workbook pages as they feel comfortable doing. Coloring the picture pages first may be a good introduction to having children write in this book.

Not all questions will be equally applicable to all children. Parents are encouraged to emphasize the areas which are pertinent to their child, and briefly read over, or skip altogether, the areas that do not pertain to the child's circumstances. If a child or family is having a particularly difficult time dealing with the emotions surrounding divorce, counseling may be beneficial. This book is not meant to replace professional counseling for children.

Many children may be resistant at first reading about such a difficult topic. others will be excited that their silent questions will be answered. If your child appears resistant to reading this book with you, you may want to read sections of it during times when they are already feeling relaxed and comfortable (before reading their regular book at bed time, while they are in the bath tub, while you are rubbing their back before they go to sleep, while listening to relaxing music, outdoors at a park, while they are eating dessert, etc.).

If your child becomes bored, upset, or agitated during reading, you may want to ask them how they are feeling. (Some children are more comfortable "showing" how they feel, such as drawing a picture, doing a short skit, demonstrating with toys or hitting a pillow.) And then, if they wish, let them know it is okay to put the book away for a while and come back to it later.

Much of how a child reacts to changes in a family is dependent upon how they see their parents reacting. Be gentle, patient and kind to yourself. Most of us did not exhibit the communication skills used by the parents in this make-believe story, but we did the best that we could. Children will respond positively when parents are self-forgiving and model how to be patient and loving to oneself.

If your child is too young to write in the workbook pages, he or she may draw pictures or representations of answers. You may also write in the answers they tell you or draw pictures they describe.

Make sure your child has drawing and writing materials available as you work through the activities together. If there is more than one child in your family, you may want to provide each with a separate piece of paper and write the question(s) at the top of each page, or order a separate book for each child.

Remember, this book is not designed for a marathon course in divorce for children. Be patient and gentle with a child going through this process. Your attitude of acceptance, regardless of your child's responses or how fast or slow he or she chooses to work through this book, is very important in helping attain the greatest possible benefit from these activities.

The story and activities provide an opportunity to become closer to your child. Completing two or three pages a day will give your child a better understanding of the divorce process, and let your child know he or she is important to you and that you will be there to help through this difficult time.

Counselors and Therapists

Counselors and therapists may want to use this book to facilitate working with children going through a divorce or dealing with their feelings after a divorce is final. It is suggested that the story and activities be presented in sections over the course of 3 to 5 therapy sessions, for the reasons outlined above. The fantasy story, coloring and workbook pages can provide a non-threatening approach to help children access their feelings about their parents separating. Therapists have also found working with this book can aid in identifying areas where a child may be having difficulty in coping with divorce.

This book also lends itself well to working with children in groups who are dealing with their parent's divorce. Once again, it is important to emphasize that there are no "right" or "wrong" answers. Group interaction and cohesiveness can be facilitated by using the workbook activities and having children share their own ideas (if they feel comfortable) with the rest of the group. Group art projects, children's own stories, poems and skits can add new dimensions to the ideas presented here, and help children develop a sense of understanding and empowerment.

Acknowledge yourself for being important in the life of a child.

How Life Once Was

A beautiful mermaid from the ocean and a strong knight from a mountain castle met on a sunny beach. They fell in love. Then they wanted to get married and be a family.

The knight moved out of his big, safe castle to be near the sea. The mermaid traded her grandmother's white pearls to a sea witch to give her legs so she could walk on land.

Finally, they were able to make special promises to each other by getting married. They wanted children in their loving family and they worked together to make a special home. They put their treasures together and believed the best about each other.

♥ The knight and the mermaid got married because they fell in love.

♥ Why do you think people get married?

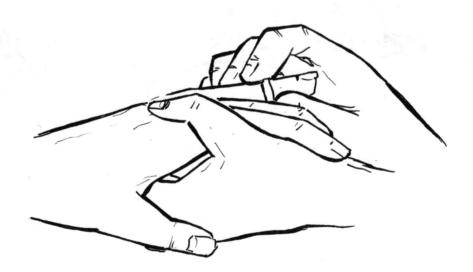

After they got married, they built a special home on the beach and had horses to ride. They had four wonderful children: Constance, Newton, Arletta, and Spartacus. Both the mermaid and the knight were very happy to have each of their children!

♥ Do you know a story about when you when you were a tiny baby? (If not, ask one of your parents or grandparents to tell you one.)

♥ Draw a picture of something you know about you as a baby.

The children were a little like each of their parents. They could breathe underwater and they could ride fast horses. They were smart and funny, just like their parents.

The mermaid and the knight loved their children very much and were very proud of each one of them.

♥ The children could swim underwater like their mother.

♥ In what ways are you like your mother?

♥ The children could ride horses like their father.

♥ In what ways are you like your father?

Then Trouble Came

One day, very dark clouds came over their home by the sea. The darkness got so thick that the flowers and the fruit trees died. Their parents were very upset about the darkness.

At night, the children heard their father say that he missed the mountains.

Their mother said that she missed living in the water. Each one blamed the other for what they were missing!

♥ The children heard their parents fighting.

♥ What did you do if you heard your parents fighting?

♥ Did anyone ever have to come and help them stop fighting (police, neighbors, or relatives)?

The angry voices got louder at night.

Everything seemed to upset both of them, and they complained about each other. Sometimes they were really, really quiet. That was even worse.

♥ The children heard their parents fighting. They didn't like it when their parents wouldn't talk to each other.

♥ How did you feel when your parents were upset with each other?

One day, Constance asked if her mother was mad at her.

Her mother gave Constance a huge hug. "Things are hard right now, but I'm not mad with you. I know I haven't been a lot of fun lately," her mother said.

"What can I do?" Constance asked.

"Thank you for asking," her mother said, "but you can't fix adult problems. Remember though, that I'll always love you."

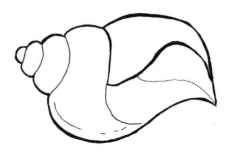

Constance was glad her mother wasn't mad about her. She was sad there was nothing she could do to make her parents happy again, so she went for a walk and fed the seagulls.

♥ Constance thought her Mom was angry at her.

♥ Think about a time you thought your parents were fighting about something that you did.

♥ Did you ask them what they were fighting about?

♥ What did they say?

A couple of days later, Spartacus was pretending to fight a fire-breathing dragon. His father walked in just as the big lamp in the living room crashed to the floor. Spartacus's pretend sword accidentally sent it flying.

CRASH! CLUNK! BANG!

Spartacus looked up. His father's face was red!

"Go to your room now!" yelled his father.

Father was usually playful and funny, but now he scolded Spartacus all the way to his bedroom.

♥ Spartacus's father punished him by yelling at him and sending him to his room.

♥ Who punished you when your parents were together?

♥ What happens when you get in trouble now?

♥ How do you feel about that?

Spartacus waited in his room. He could hear loud, blaming voices. Then it was quiet. He heard a knock on his door, and his father came in.

"I'm sorry, Spart," said the knight. "You know the rule about playing with the sword in the house, but that's no excuse for me to yell."

"You're never any fun anymore! And you never play with me!" yelled Spartacus.

His father sat on the floor and pulled him close.

"I wish I felt more like playing, too," his father said. "One day soon I'll be back to my happy self. I want to know how you feel. It's important to me. I may not always like what you tell me, but that's okay."

♥ Spartacus's father said he wanted to hear how his son was feeling even if his feelings weren't always easy for him to hear about.

♥ Circle feelings you have had.

Comfortable feelings

amused, great, confident, encouraged, helpful, satisfied, infatuated, glad, accepted, enthusiastic, hopeful, irresistible, noble, tender, industrious, proud, impressed, lovable, affectionate, inspired, competent, excited, grateful, capable, relaxed, good, blissful, thoughtful, ecstatic, creative, pleased, relieved, optimistic, content, delighted, eager, appreciated, expectant, accepted, mellow, triumphant, successful, determined, balanced, forgiving, joyful, loved, efficient, happy, proud, comfortable, sympathetic, surprised, caring, graceful, giggly, nurturing, respected, determined

In-between feelings

ambivalent, mischievous, apathetic, sleepy, nostalgic, tempted, undecided, conniving, timid, shocked, boastful, smug, indecisive, passive, skeptical, indifferent, apologetic, nonchalant, interested, perplexed

Uncomfortable feelings

confused, left out, depressed, incapable, dissatisfied, bashful, nauseated, inadequate, argumentative, disrespectful, defeated, discouraged, disappointed, rejected, miserable, unloved, nervous, suspicious, resentful, enraged, clumsy, agonized, accused, overworked, embarrassed, threatened, disgusted, obstinate, overwhelmed, contemptuous, hopeless, vulnerable, unhappy, aggravated, insignificant, withdrawn, worried, insecure, useless, helpless, scared, frustrated, anxious, negative, tired, hostile, guilty, cranky, sad, lonely, bored, angry, sick, hurt, foolish, paranoid, jealous, exasperated, competitive, horrified, hysterical, pressured, homesick, put down, worthless, miserable, exhausted, aggressive, regretful, sulky, greedy, unhappy, hopeless, frightened, angry, scared, lonely, ignored, trapped, embarrassed, frightened, apprehensive, disappointed

Newton heard the shouting. His stomach felt sick. He turned the volume up on his video game and sat a little closer to the screen.

♥ When Newton felt sad and scared, his stomach hurt.

♥ When you feel upset do you ever have stomach aches? Headaches?

♥ How does your body feel when you are angry?

♥ Or happy?

♥ Or sad?

♥ Or afraid?

♥ Or excited?

♥ Or loved?

When Arletta heard all the noise, she went to her special place (a corner in her room) and drew a picture of an ugly troll. She used a bright green crayon for the troll and a black one for the dark clouds in the sky.

♥ Arletta had a special place she likes to go to be alone.

♥ Do you have a special place you like to go to think? (Tree house, bedroom, backyard, secret hiding place, or _____)

Mom and dad Tell the Kids

Their parents spent less time together. Sometimes one would leave and then come back home. They were sad and angry most of the time.

♥ As the mermaid and the knight fought more and more, sometimes one of them would leave for a while.

♥ If your parents lived apart before they divorced, how did you feel? (You can use the lists of feeling words on page 26.)

One night, after dinner, the knight and the mermaid called all the children into the living room. It was dark as nighttime.

Everyone sat down. Constance tied her shoelaces perfectly. Newton pretended to read a book. Spartacus slid off the couch and lay down on the floor with his feet up on the cushions. Arletta scooted over so his feet wouldn't hit Kitty Cat.

"Your mother and I have something to tell you," their father said. "This isn't easy for us."

Newton looked up from his phone and even Spartacus looked upside down at his father.

"Your dad and I have decided that we can't live together anymore," said their mother.

"Divorce?" Spartacus blurted out.

"Spart! Be quiet!" snapped Constance.

"It looks that way," said their father. "Any questions? We'll answer them the best we can. We haven't figured everything out yet, but ask away."

♥ Both parents told the kids they were getting divorced. Sometimes only one parent tells the kids, or sometimes someone else does.

♥ Who told you your parents were getting divorced?

♥ Did you feel —

- Sad
- Worried
- Ignored
- Happy
- Nervous
- Guilty
- Angry
- Confused
- Ashamed
- Frightened
- Safe
- Scared
- Trapped
- Curious
- Apprehensive
- Uncertain
- Lonely
- Embarrassed
- Hurt
- Disappointed

(You can look back to page 27 for more feeling words.)

"Don't you love each other anymore?" Arletta could barely choke out the words. "Don't you love *us* anymore?"

"Your father and I can't live together anymore," answered their mother, "but no matter how we feel about each other, we'll always love you no matter what."

"Aren't we a family anymore?" asked Constance.

"Well," said their mother, "now you'll have two families. You'll always be our children and we'll take care of you."

"If you're scared or confused, said the knight, "there are other people you can talk to as well."

♥ The kids had lots of people to talk to.

♥ Who do you want to talk to when you feel bad?

__a friend   __your parent   __your pet
__a teacher   __a counselor   __a coach
__a grandparent   __an aunt   __an uncle
__your baby-sitter   __a cousin   __a parent's friend
__a stuffed animal   __a school counselor   __your journal
__kids at a divorce
    support group

"Where will we live?"

"Who will take care of us?"

"Will we have to move?"

"Do Grandma and Grandpa know?"

"Why do you want a divorce?"

Constance started crying.

"Connie, we're all sad. It's okay to cry," said the mermaid. "You'll spend some of your time with me and some with your father. You'll always be with someone who loves you very much."

Constance couldn't imagine living away from either of her parents. How would her parents feel when she hugged and kissed the other one good-bye? Did either of her parents want her to take sides? She felt confused.

♥ Constance felt scared and confused. She couldn't imagine living at two houses.

♥ Most kids feel confused when their parents are getting divorced. What part was confusing to you?

♥ It's okay to keep on loving both your parents.

♥ Has it ever felt strange to show one parent you love them in front of the other?

Newton pretended to read a book, again.

"Any questions, Newt?" asked his father.

"My friend Jake's father is a sailor and he went away and never came back," Newton said, from behing his book.

"Some parents feel so guilty or so sad, that they don't call or see their kids because it's too hard for them," Father said, "but I'll always be here for you. You can call me anytime you are at your mother's home, and you can call her anytime you are with me. We both love you very much."

♥ Newton was glad that his father would still spend time with him, but he knew he'd miss him sometimes, too.

♥ How can you feel close to the parent you're not with?

- Write notes in a journal
- Save school work and art for them
- Write stories for them
- Phone them
- Start a scrapbook
- Have a picture of them in your room
- Give them a picture of you
- Make up a song for them
- Make a recording of your voice
- Let them know about up-coming school events
- Draw pictures

- Start a private blog
- Write poems
- Collect jokes they might like
- Text messages or pictures
- Skype or FaceTime
- Leave voicemails
- Email
- Make a video of yourself or an activity
- Play an online game with them
- Make plans to do something with them

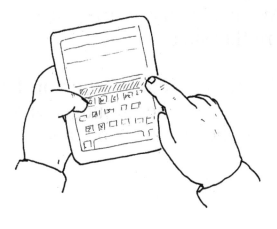

"Can I bring Kitty Cat if we move?" asked Arletta.

"She can stay at your dad's," said their mother. "You can get a new catfish, or maybe a dolphin at my house."

"What if you can't agree on when we'll be with each of you?" Arletta asked.

"There are people who can help us decide," Father said. "If we can't agree, then a judge will listen to each of us. The judge will make the last decision, and everyone has to obey those rules."

♥ There are some things parents might need help deciding:

How much time kids will spend with each parent.

What schools and which doctors children will go to.

How much money one parent gives to the other to help pay for things children need.

How much money one parent gives the other to help them out until they can make enough money on their own.

♥ Were you worried your parents might fight about some things?

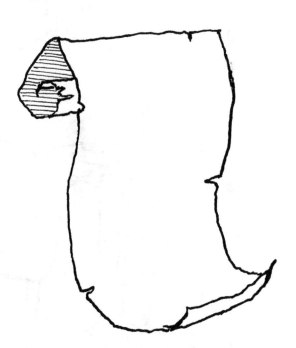

The kids were all glad that the talk was over.

Constance climbed into her mother's lap.

Spartacus grabbed his ball and mitt and went outside.

Newton went to his room to play a video game.

Arletta took Kitty Cat outside and sat where the garden used to be before it got so dark.

♥ Who helped your parents with their divorce?

___ Counselor or therapist (A person trained to help people talk about their feelings)

___ Mediator (A person who helps parents divide belongings, money, and time with children)

___ Attorney/Lawyer (A person who gives your parents advice and may talk to the judge for your parent)

___ Judge (The person who makes the last decision about how things are divided up, and which parent takes care of the children. The judge is the person who says the divorce is final.)

♥ Has the judge written out the rules and signed a paper saying that the divorce is done yet?

The Children's Reactions

Spartacus

Spartacus stomped down the sidewalk. *It's not fair!* He thought. *No one asked me if I wanted Mom and Dad to get divorced!*

♥ Draw a picture of how you felt when you found out your parents were getting divorced.

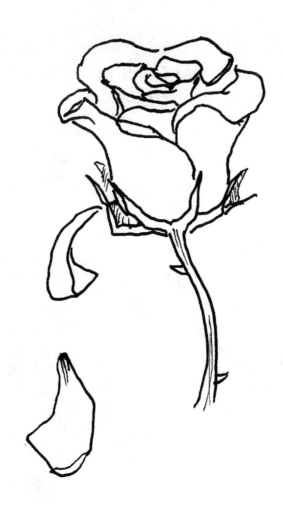

Spartacus burst through the door. He threw his ball at the door and yelled, "You're mean! You don't love me anymore!"

His father was surprised. "Come here, Spart!" he said, in a stern voice. "What's going on? You sound really angry."

"I'm mad!" Spartacus yelled. "I'm mad at you and Mom and everybody!"

His father sat down on the floor and patted the spot next to him. Spartacus just stood there, arms crossed, staring at the wall, with tears running down his cheeks.

"Son," the knight said, "It's all right to feel angry, and disappointed. I always love you, even when you're angry and hurt, but it's not all right to show your anger in ways that might hurt people or things. What's another way to get your anger out?"

♥ Spartacus was very angry. Some of the ways he showed he was mad were okay, but other ways were not.

♥ What things would you like to do to help get your angry feelings out?

___ Talk to someone
___ Write a story
___ Punch a punching bag
___ Shoot baskets
___ Yell into a pillow
___ Swim
___ Go for a walk
___ Throw a ball
___ Cry
___ Have someone hold you
___ Jump on a trampoline
___ Hit clay
___ Draw a picture
___ Write angry feelings on paper and then stomp it, poke holes in it, or flush it down the toilet.

___ Run
___ Dance
___ Sit alone
___ Listen to music
___ Hit a stuffed animal
___ Play video games
___ Make something to eat
___ Play a musical instrument
___ Watch a movie
___ Write an angry feeling on a rock and throw it into a lake, river or ocean.
___ Say really angry words alone with your door closed

"Would you like to hit the punching bag with me?" The knight said.

"If you want," Spartacus said, as they headed outside.

"You know your Mom and I aren't getting divorced because of anything you've done, don't you?"

"Yeah," he mumbled.

"And there's nothing you can do to get us to stay together, either," said his father.

Spartacus looked up surprised. "Yeah, I know," he said.

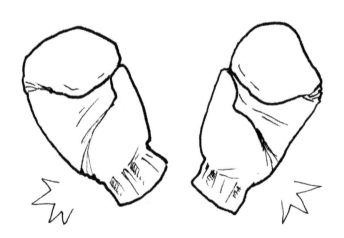

♥ Spartacus was glad his father helped him think of things he could do when he was upset.

♥ What are some things you like to do with your dad?

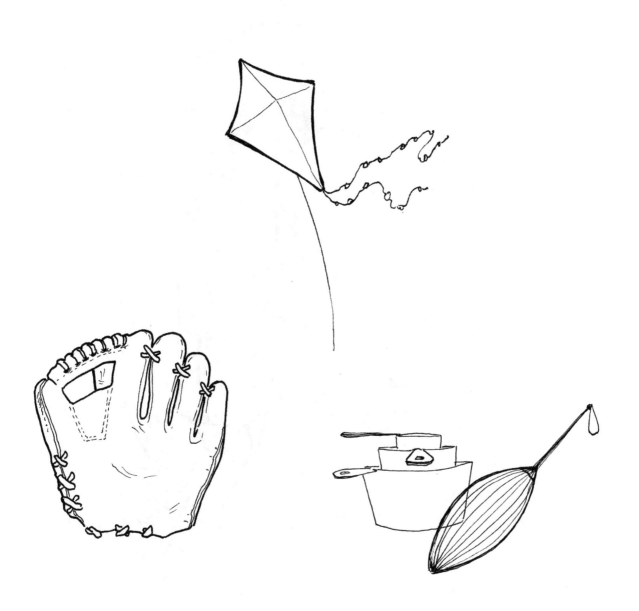

"Lots of kids hope they can get their parents back together," his father said. "Some by being extra good, other ones by making trouble."

"Like Constance is pretending to be really good. Yuck!!" Spartacus said.

"More like that time you made monsters spray out of a water bottle when Arletta was afraid of the dark," his father said.

Spartacus smiled and laced up his gloves. He growled and attacked the punching bag. His dad joined in.

♥ Spartacus told his father he was mad at his sister.

♥ Was it hard sometimes to get along with a brother or sister when your parents were divorcing?

♥ What did your brother or sister do that REALLY bothered you?

Constance

"Aren't families supposed to stay together no matter what?" Constance asked her. "I'm never going to get divorced when I grow up!"

"Things don't always work out the way we plan," her mother said. "Your father and I have always done the very best we could do at the time."

♥ Even though Constance usually thought she was too big to sit in her mother's lap, when she felt sad she liked cuddling and talking with her.

♥ What things does your mother do that make you feel special and loved?

Constance didn't like her family changing. When she felt sad she talked to her counselor, Dr. Huggs. Dr. Huggs was fun and taught her how to feel better by doing things that she liked. This helped her not worry so much.

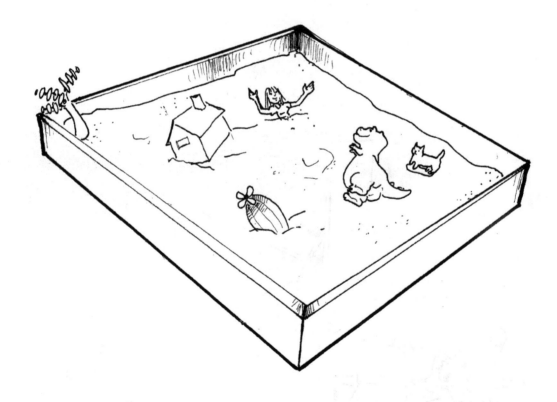

♥ Constance found lots of things that helped her feel better.

♥ There are things you can do to feel better:

- Talk to a friend
- Write a story
- Count slowly to ten
- Breathe deeply
- Play with clay
- Go to the batting cages
- Paint a picture
- Take a walk with someone
- Go swimming (with supervision)
- Play outdoors
- Play with a pet
- Listen to music
- Dance
- Play sports
- Watch animals
- Rollerblade
- Pray
- Talk to your Guardian Angel
- Make something for an upcoming holiday
- Learn a new sport
- Go skateboarding or bicycling
- Build or make something
- Read
- Call or email someone you love
- Make a card for someone
- Visit a friend
- Organize your room
- Create a treasure hunt
- Finger paint
- Write on the sidewalk with chalk
- Plant some seeds
- Have someone take you to a park and feed the ducks
- Find animals in the clouds
- Make a special sandwich
- Watch your favorite movie
- Get or give a hug
- Play games on the computer

One day, her mother complained to Constance about her father. "And if only he would—" she began, but Constance stopped her.

"Mom, if you have something bad to say about Dad, you need to tell him or another adult. I don't want to hear bad things about either one of you."

"You're right," her mother said. "I bet that was hard for you to tell me. Even when I feel bad, I still love you."

♥ It was hard for Constance to tell her mother she didn't want to hear bad things about her dad.

♥ Have either of your parents told you bad things about the other one?

♥ What did you say or do?

♥ What would you like to do?

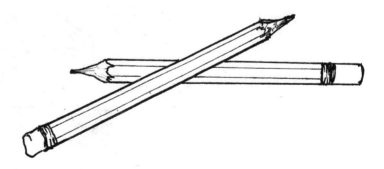

Newton

The house was different now. It was dark and sad. Boxes were piled up everywhere.

Newton looked up things on his phone or computer. He played video games and made up jokes with his friend Cassidy. They didn't talk about the divorce. Newton liked that.

♥ Newton found ways to feel better.

♥ Did you have to move?

♥ Which of your parents moved out?

♥ Do you spend time with each of your parents?

♥ How do you feel about that?

Newton's teacher, Ms. Johnson, worried about him. He was turning in homework late and stared out the window during class.

He couldn't understand why his parents were divorcing. He was surprised that people would divorce over arguing. He liked to argue with his friends, but they didn't get angry with each other. They thought it was fun!

♥ Newton wondered *WHY* about many parts of his parents' divorce.

♥ What things have you wondered *WHY* about?

"It's hard when we don't understand something," his teacher said.

"If I try hard enough," Newton said, "I should understand it."

"Well, some things do work that way." His teacher smiled. "Like learning math, but other things don't. Sometimes we have to work on finding out how to feel better, and not work so hard on figuring out the *WHY*."

"But I always like figuring out the *WHY*," Newton said.

His teacher laughed, "I know. That's one of the things that makes you so special. But sometimes we don't ever completely understand *WHY*."

She gave him a big hug, that made him feel better even if he didn't know exactly *WHY*.

♥ Newton was confused and frustrated because he didn't have all the answers he wanted. He also felt comforted by his teacher, even though he still felt confused.

♥ Sometimes we feel two different feelings at once.

♥ It is okay to feel two different feelings at the same time.

Such as:

Surprised and Sad
Hopeful and Disappointed
Angry and Relieved
Loving and Mad

♥ What two different feelings have you felt?

_____and_____

_____and_____

_____and_____

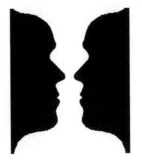

Arletta

Arletta drew pictures of her whole family up in a castle on the mountain with a swimming pool for her mother. She drew pictures of the whole family under the sea, living in a giant bubble for her father. She drew pictures of the sun coming out from behind the clouds at the beach where they lived now.

♥ Arletta wanted things to go back the way they were. Most kids want their family back together even when they know it won't happen.

♥ Did you hope your parents would get back together?

♥ Who did you talk to about that?

She took the pictures to her mother.

"Look what I made for you," she said.

The mermaid smiled. "This is hard for you, isn't it?" she asked.

Arletta shrugged. She didn't want her mother to feel bad for her.

"I want everyone to be happy right now," she said, softly.

♥ Arletta didn't like to see her parents unhappy.

♥ Have you seen your parents cry?

♥ How do you feel when they cried?

♥ Do you know that crying can sometimes make grownups feel better, too?

"Remember that caterpillar," her mother asked, "the one you caught last spring?"

"He was fuzzy and green," Arletta smiled, "and moved like an accordion."

"And he made a cocoon, remember?"

"Yeah, I remember," she said.

"And you really wanted to open it and let him out?"

Arletta nodded.

"What did I say?"

"If I made him hurry," Arletta frowned, "he'd never be a butterfly."

"And did he finally come out?"

"He was beautiful!" Arletta beamed.

"Well, sometimes sadness is like that," her mother said. "We can't hurry it or make it better as quick as we'd like."

"So, some day you and Dad will be happy again?" she asked.

"That's the plan," she said, and gave her a hug.

♥ Arletta's mother explained about sadness by telling her a story.

♥ What things does your mother do to make you feel special and loved?

"We're hoping we'll all be happier," her mother said.

"What if you're not?" Arletta said.

"Some parents choose to stay mad at each other," her mother agreed.

"Will you?' Arletta asked.

"That's up to me," her mother said. "I have friends under the sea, books and a counselor to help me choose to stop being angry and be happy again."

"Auntie says addictions can make people unhappy," Arletta said. "What's an addiction?"

Her mother took a deep breath. "When someone can't stop doing something that makes them and the people close to them sad," said her mother. "Addictions can be to alcohol, drugs or other things that hurt them."

♥ When someone can't stop doing something that hurts them, they may have the disease of addiction.

♥ If you know someone with an addiction, draw a picture of what you think it looks like, or how it makes you feel.

"Will Dad stop being angry too?" Arletta asked.

"It's up to each of us," the mermaid said. "We both have to be kind to ourselves."

"Like when I got mad at Paul for accidentally bumping me in line because I already felt embarrassed about accidentally leaving the cap off of Sarnia's markers?"

"Exactly!" her mother said. "When we're upset with ourselves, we get madder at other people."

♥ Arletta got really mad over a little thing because she was already upset about something else.

♥ What things do you get mad about?

♥ Draw a picture of a time you got extra mad because you were already feeling bad about something else.

"I do things to make myself feel happier," Arletta said.

"Yes, you do," her mother said. "I've seen you draw pictures and write stories and play with Kitty Cat and make up plays with your friends. You are very creative!" She kissed her forehead.

♥ Draw a picture of yourself doing something that makes you feel better.

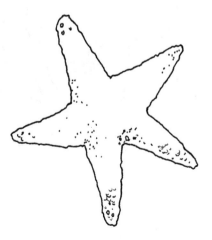

After the Divorce

Spartacus

At first, it felt strange living in new places, but soon the children liked their new homes, especially Spartacus.

At his father's home he explored the woods with his toy sword. He pretended he was a knight, rescuing anyone in trouble.

He also liked having new things, like a bright flashlight to shine in the forest at night.

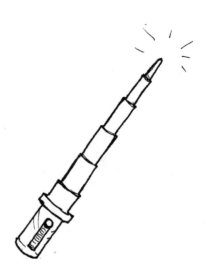

♥ Spartacus liked having some new things at his father's house.

♥ What special things do you have at your dad's house?

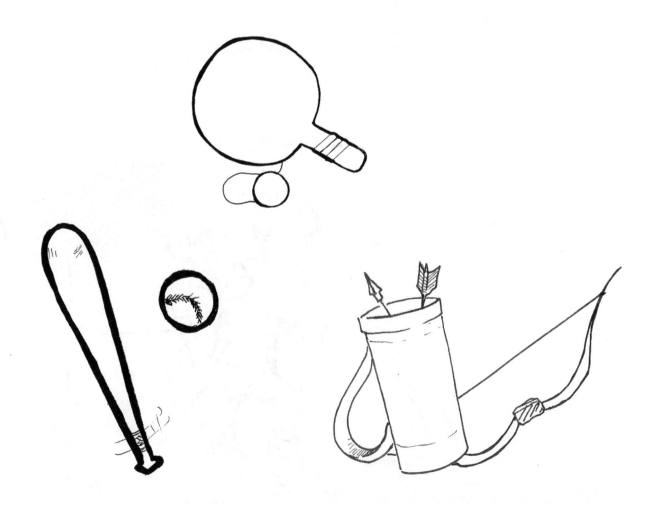

At his mom's house, he played water polo and used his searchlight to explore underwater caves.

"But Dad would let me go alone!" Spartacus argued with his mom.

"Our rules are different," his mom said.

♥ Spartacus got used to having different rules at each house just like he learned to raise his hand at school but not at home.

♥ What rules are different at each of your parents' homes?

♥ How do you feel about those rules being different?

Spartacus tried to scare his dad's new girlfriend with a frog. He didn't think he'd like her much.

"Oh, an enchanted prince!" she said, and kissed it on the nose.

Spartacus laughed. He thought she was silly!

She never tried to boss him around. It was only up to his dad to tell him what to do. That was one of his dad's rules that he liked best.

♥ Spartacus wouldn't have liked it if his dad's new friend had tried to tell him what to do.

♥ If you've met one of your parent's new dates how did you feel?

♥ What did you do?

Constance

Constance missed her old house, but she liked spending more time with her grandparents.

"Grandma," Constance said. "Mom wants me to tell Dad things for her. I don't want to."

"That's got to be hard," Grandma said.

"Yeah, and they both complain to me about each other!" Constance said. "They both blame the other for not having enough money."

"Those are grown-up problems, not yours," Grandma said. "You can always talk to me when you feel bad."

♥ Constance didn't like hearing her parents fight about money. Sometimes she was disappointed that she couldn't get something she wanted.

♥ How do your parents spend money differently now?

♥ How do you feel about that?

♥ If your parents still fight about money, how do you feel about that?

"What chores do you choose for this week?" The mermaid asked the children at their Sunday afternoon family meeting.

"I'm tired of doing it all!" Constance said.

"Constance," her mother said, "we're all going to pitch in. I'm going to give you stars and rewards."

"Spartacus always forgets," complained Newton.

"That's why I'll keep track and remind you. I'll give you each your stars," their mom said.

"I want to stay up later," said Newton.

"I want to go to the skate park," Spartacus said.

"I want to go sailing with just you," said Constance.

"I want to go to the art museum with you," Arletta said.

"Wait! Wait! One at a time," the mermaid laughed.

♥ Constance was happy her mother made everyone help out.

♥ What problems have you talked about with each parent?

♥ How did you solve the problems?

♥ What problems would you still like to talk about?

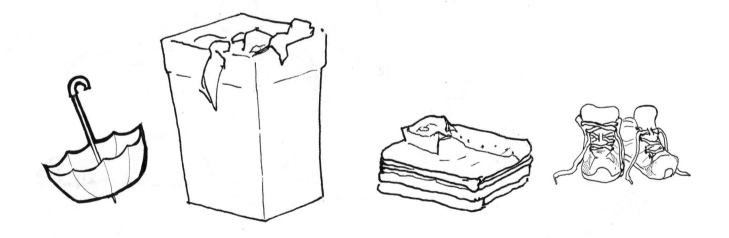

"You can't take your video game box to Mom's!" Constance yelled at Newton.

Newton rolled his eyes.

"Constance," the knight said, "Don't try to parent Newton. That's my job. You can both keep special things at each house."

"But he thinks—."

The knight did a little drum roll with his fingers and said, "Constance, what do you want to keep at my house?"

Constance dropped her back pack and unzipped it. She pulled out her origami book and slid it back in her bookcase.

♥ Constance had special things at each of her parents' homes.

♥ Draw a picture of something special at your mom's house.

♥ Draw a picture of something special at your dad's house.

Constance read a text message. "Going to volleyball practice?" Vanessa asked.

"Yeah." Constance tapped her phone. "C U there." She added a smiley face.

She was glad she'd joined the team and met her new friend.

♥ **What groups do you belong to?**

___ School	___ Boy's and Girl's Club
___ Scouts	___ Choir/Chorus
___ Band	___ Equestrian/Riding
___ Sport _____	___ Dance
___ Gymnastics	___ Martial arts
___ Computer class	___ House of Worship
___ Cooking class	___ A Volunteer Group
___ Theater	___ Art Class
	_____

♥ **Draw a picture of your group.**

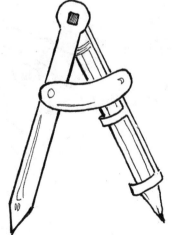

"You're always busy!" Constance complained to her father.

The knight stopped stirring pizza sauce for dinner and knelt down. "What would you like to do just with me?" he asked.

Constance shrugged.

"Well, last week you swam to look for buried treasure in that old ship with your mom. How about we go riding and look for dragon eggs?"

"Dragon eggs?! Just us?" Constance did a little happy dance.

Her father laughed. "Yes. Just us."

♥ Constance loved spending time alone with each parent when they weren't doing errands or chores.

♥ What is something that doesn't cost much money that you would like to do with one of your parents?

- Play a video game
- Watch a movie or cartoon
- Read a book
- Go camping or fishing
- Draw with chalk on sidewalk
- Blow bubbles
- Listen to stories about when they were a kid
- Color
- Make up a play
- Swing at the park
- Play catch
- Go watch trains or airplanes
- Make up songs or jokes
- Learn to draw with a book or internet site
- Go for a walk
- Make a garden
- Get a book from the library
- Visit a museum or art gallery
- Cook or bake
- Swim
- Find constellations of stars at night
- Pick wildflowers
- Hike
- Go bird watching
- Go to a skate park
- Paint big posters

- Make collages out of magazine pictures
- Learn to count in another language
- Play a guessing game
- Organize your room with containers
- Play cards
- Find animals in the clouds
- Make up a recipe and give it your name
- Have a picnic outside or under the table
- Bicycle or rollerblade
- Tell riddles
- Make up a game
- Sing or play percussion along with a CD
- Check out homework help apps
- Play hide and seek
- Learn magic tricks
- Visit relatives
- Help volunteer
- Build something with connecting toys
- Make up your own calligraphy
- Wash the car
- Play with a pet
- Plan a vacation
- Find new kid games online,
- Make a video for a grandparent,
-  _____

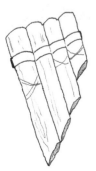

Newton

Newton was the first to memorize both of his new addresses. He had a special shelf for his games at each house.

"Do you have this game at your dad's?" his mom asked, as she gave him another present.

Newton felt bad. "Mom, I like being with you because I love you, not because you buy me stuff."

"You don't like it?" his mother asked.

"Yeah, thanks!" Newton said. "I just wanted you to know I'd want to be with you no matter what."

He looked down at the game case and smiled. "And there's a new version coming out next month, just so you know." He made a fake smile.

The mermaid laughed. So did Newton.

"Wanna play?" Newton asked.

♥ It was hard for Newton to talk to Mom about buying so many presents.

♥ Did it sometimes feel like either of your parents were trying to make you like them more by giving you presents?

♥ If so, how did you feel?

Newton used homework help apps and computer sites to make his homework more fun. He liked getting his papers back with good grades. He also liked helping his friends understand their homework.

He still liked to spend time alone and liked quiet time at both the houses.

♥ Newton didn't have to change schools, but sometimes kids have to.

♥ Did you have to change schools?

♥ If so, was it hard or easy to make new friends?

♥ What new friends did you meet?

♥ Was it easy or hard to find your new classroom?

♥ Was your new class ahead or behind your old class?

♥ How did you feel about that?

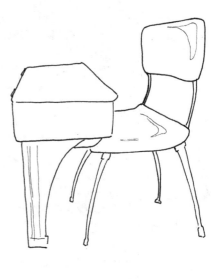

Newton was happy that the fighting stopped. He liked things quiet and peaceful.

The judge had made a special rule about not drinking alcohol around the kids.

For a long time, his dad didn't drink when he was with them, but at Sunday's backyard barbeque he saw his father drinking alcohol.

Newton didn't want to embarrass him at the party, so the next day he wrote a note to both his parents about the rules. He was afraid that they might be mad at him, but he didn't want to lose out on time with his father.

"Thanks for the note, Newt," his dad said. He looked a little annoyed, but his voice was nice. "I promise to do better. I always want to know how you feel."

Newton gave him a high five and felt better.

♥ Judges don't always make special rules. The judge did made a special rule for the knight.

♥ Did the judge make any special rules that your parents are supposed to follow?

Yes  No

Where your parents are supposed to meet to pick you up?
No drinking or using drugs around the children?
No spanking?
To have someone else with them when they visit you?
To not say bad things about the other parent in front of you?

♥ What would you do if your parents disobeyed the judge's rule?

Newton liked the paper calendar in the kitchen that showed when he was going to be at each parent's home.

The purple days were with dad, the green ones with mom. He liked planning ahead, especially for holidays.

He liked celebrating every holiday two times. Even his birthday!

♥ Newton liked to check the colors on the calendar to see which house he would be at next weekend.

♥ Is there a calendar you can look at to know when you are going to be with each parent?

♥ Where would you like to put that calendar?

Arletta

Arletta made Kitty Cat a bed at her father's home. She got a new pet dolphin at her mother's. She drew pictures of make-believe adventures with both her pets.

She put sparkly lights on the water for the underwater holidays of the tides. She picked grapes and apples on the mountain for the harvest festivals. She really liked celebrating her birthday at each house.

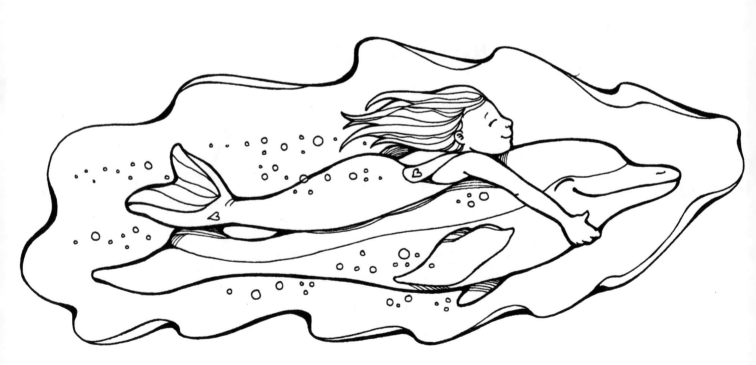

♥ Holidays might be different at each house. Arletta found out she liked celebrating at each of her parent's homes.

♥ How are holidays celebrated differently now that your parents are divorced?

♥ How do you celebrate your birthday now?

"Good night, Mom. I miss you, too," Arletta said to the big screen. "I'll text you tomorrow."

When she missed the parent she wasn't with, she sometimes made cards and pictures for them. Each parent called to say "good night" when she was at the other one's home.

One night, when her father called to say "good night," Arletta cried because she missed him.

"It's okay to be sad," the knight said. "Sometimes I cry, too. It goes away in a little bit."

"Do you feel better after you cry?" she asked.

"Yes. That's one way to change how I feel. I also go to the gym and watch TV," her father said.

"I feel better now," Arletta said. "Thank you for talking with me."

"Good night, Sweetie," her dad said. "I will always love you. No matter whatever else changes, that never will."

♥ Arletta knew she was always loved, no matter what.

♥ Draw a picture of being loved by both parents, even though they're divorced.

Constance, Newton, Arletta, and Spartacus each have their own feelings about their parents' divorce. And each one found different ways to handle their feelings. They each had special things at each new home.

Best of all, they can say, "My parents still love me, even though they're getting divorced."

THE END

About the author

Lois V. Nightingale, Ph. D. is a licensed Psychologist, and a Marriage, Child and Family Therapist in Yorba Linda California. She has been helping individuals and families for over thirty years.

She is a nationally recognized speaker and an award-winning writer. She has made many professional appearances on local, national and international television helping to educate parents and teaching better communication to families.

As a divorced single mother of two children, she realizes the importance of a story that children can relate to. A story that also teaches coping skills and better ways to handle the confusion of divorce and gives children the opportunity to express their own feelings.

It is her goal to help families find resources to assist them through changes. She believes that if children receive support, encouragement, and a safe place to express their feelings during times of change and loss, many of the negative long-term effects of these childhood disruptions can be avoided. Children can learn they are lovable and strong. Dr. Nightingale feels that parents have a responsibility to model for their children (even in the face of adversity and change) that there are always opportunities to become more caring, compassionate and self-assured individuals. You can follow Dr. Nightingale on Twitter @Drdrloisn.

Published by:

Nightingale Rose Publications
16960 East Bastanchury Road, Suite J
Yorba Linda, California 92886

CPSIA information can be obtained
at www.ICGtesting.com
Printed in the USA
LVHW022144200921
698316LV00022B/563